The
Brightest
Star of All

The Brightest Star of All

Christmas Stories for the Family

CARRIE PAPA

Abingdon Press
Nashville

THE BRIGHTEST STAR OF ALL
CHRISTMAS STORIES FOR THE FAMILY

This book is printed on acid-free paper.

Library of Congress Cataloging-in-Publication Data

Papa, Carrie, 1926-
  The brightest star of all : Christmas stories for the family / Carrie Papa.
    p. cm.
  ISBN 978-0-687-64813-9 (binding: adhesive-perfect : alk. paper)
  1. Christmas. 2. Family–Religious life. 3. Christmas stories. I. Title.

  BV45.P353 2008
  242'.335–dc22

                                    2008010636

08 09 10 11 12 13 14 15 16 17—10 9 8 7 6 5 4 3 2 1
MANUFACTURED IN THE UNITED STATES OF AMERICA

For Jo and Lee Ann

CONTENTS

The
Power
of Stories

Among the many ways that God calls to us is through the symbolic and compelling use of stories and parables. The beauty and power of simple narratives to teach spiritual truths and moral lessons is a charming means of bringing new understanding and thoughtful appreciation to sacred writings.

The many Christmas stories that developed through the years and throughout the world have become part of our culture, expressing the deep spiritual significance of the birth of Christ. Since people think in tangible pictures rather than in vague theories, stories help make abstract concepts such as beauty, faith, hope, and love real by using concrete images. These simple accounts use the plain, everyday elements of life to create an immediate impression that moves us from what we know to that which we have not yet thought about. Our thinking is led from the material to the spiritual as we go from the things we see to the invisible world of ideas. The stories of Christmas convey messages that speak to our hearts, enliven our sympathies, and compel us to follow.

These little stories, created by Christians to help explain and dramatize the biblical story of Christmas, are often referred to as legends. Derived from the Latin, the medieval meaning of the word *legend* was "reading" or "lesson." At a time when few people were able to read or write, earthly stories were used to convey heavenly meanings. Just as the great truths of Christianity were told through the medium of art in the majestic cathedrals of the Middle Ages (sometimes called "Bibles in Stone"), legends told by one person to another became a way of making the conceptual real.

These charming tales grew out of people's need to express the ideals of the gospel. Many of the best-known stories are found throughout the Christian world; they have traveled from country to country and generation to generation. Although the main character may change from a poor little shepherd girl to an impoverished Mexican boy, or from a small branch of mistletoe to a tall fir, the essence of the story remains the same—a mirror of virtue.

The unsophisticated personalities in these tales exemplify the aims and dreams of people everywhere. The characters' humility, generosity, and compassion overcome the evil and wickedness in the world. The main players in these modest dramas—whether people, plants, or animals—take on human characteristics that are part of the charm of the story. They are kind, meek, forgiving. Their examples present goodness as a desirable quality to be practiced in everyday life. The goal of the stories is less to show what the central figure does than to show us what *we* could be doing in response to God's love. The stories thus give us models to follow and help draw us nearer to God. In particular, the Nativity stories help increase our understanding of the great spiritual truths of the Christmas narrative.

The tales present an inviting picture, showing how all things are related to one another and act in accordance with God's will to achieve the triumph of good over evil. They crystallize the depth and power of God's love for all humanity through the gift of the Christ Child. No matter where these enchanting stories of Christmas take us, they always lead us back to the Infant of Bethlehem with a new love and a desire to worship him.

A Note to Parents and Teachers

To make the Christmas stories as meaningful and as helpful as possible in both family and group settings, each chapter is followed by suggestions for sharing the themes. Activities and crafts that complement the legends can be adapted for family gatherings, children's programs, youth groups, and intergenerational programs. Suggestions requiring minimal preparation, materials, and expense have been selected because the goal is to unite families and groups by enjoying simple activities and special times together. Families and community groups may want to combine some of the ideas into a social evening of activities and friendship.

The Christmas Story as Told in the Bible

The Birth of Jesus

In those days Caesar Augustus issued a decree that a census should be taken of the entire Roman world. (This was the first census that took place while Quirinius was governor of Syria.) And everyone went to his own town to register.

So Joseph also went up from the town of Nazareth in Galilee to Judea, to Bethlehem the town of David, because he belonged to the house and line of David. He went there to register with Mary, who was pledged to be married to him and was expecting a child. While they were there, the time came for the baby to be born, and she gave birth to her firstborn, a son. She wrapped him in cloths and placed him in a manger, because there was no room for them in the inn (Luke 2:1-7).

The Shepherds and the Angels

And there were shepherds living out in the fields nearby, keeping watch over their flocks at night. An angel of the Lord appeared to them, and the glory of the Lord shone around them, and they were terrified. But the angel said to them, "Do not be afraid. I bring you good news of great joy that will be for all the people. Today in the town of David a Savior has been born to you; he is Christ the Lord. This will be a sign to you: You will find a baby wrapped in cloths and lying in a manger."

Suddenly a great company of the heavenly host appeared with the angel, praising God and saying,

"Glory to God in the highest,
  and on earth peace to men on whom his favor rests."

When the angels had left them and gone into heaven, the shepherds said to one another, "Let's go to Bethlehem and see this thing that has happened, which the Lord has told us about."

So they hurried off and found Mary and Joseph, and the baby, who was lying in the manger. When they had seen him, they spread the word concerning what had been told them about this child, and all who heard it were amazed at what the shepherds said to them. But Mary treasured up all these things and pondered them in her heart. The shepherds returned, glorifying and praising God for all the things they had heard and seen, which were just as they had been told (Luke 2:8-20).

The Visit of the Magi

After Jesus was born in Bethlehem in Judea, during the time of King Herod, Magi from the east came to Jerusalem and asked, "Where is the one who has been born king of the Jews? We saw his star in the east and have come to worship him."

When King Herod heard this he was disturbed, and all Jerusalem with him. When he had called together all the people's chief priests and teachers of the law, he asked them where the Christ was to be born. "In Bethlehem in Judea," they replied, "for this is what the prophet has written:

" 'But you, Bethlehem, in the land of Judah,
    are by no means least among the
        rulers of Judah;
for out of you will come a ruler
    who will be the shepherd of my
        people Israel.' "

Then Herod called the Magi secretly and found out from them the exact time the star had appeared. He sent them to Bethlehem and said, "Go and make a careful search for the child. As soon as you find him, report to me, so that I too may go and worship him."

After they had heard the king, they went on their way, and the star they had seen in the east went ahead of them until it stopped over the place where the child was. When they saw the star, they were overjoyed. On coming to the house, they saw the child with his mother Mary, and they bowed down and worshiped him. Then they opened their treasures and presented him with gifts of gold and of incense and of myrrh. And having been warned in a dream not to go back to Herod, they returned to their country by another route (Matthew 2:1-12).

The Escape to Egypt

When they had gone, an angel of the Lord appeared to Joseph in a dream. "Get up," he said, "take the child and his mother and escape to Egypt. Stay there until I tell you, for Herod is going to search for the child to kill him."

So he got up, took the child and his mother during the night and left for Egypt, where he stayed until the death of Herod. And so was fulfilled what the Lord had said through the prophet: "Out of Egypt I called my son" (Matthew 2:13-15).

CHAPTER ONE

Stories About Light

The people walking in the darkness
       have seen a great light;
on those living in the land of the shadow of death
       a light has dawned....
For to us a child is born,
       to us a son is given,
       and the government will be on his shoulders.
And he will be called
       Wonderful Counselor, Mighty God,
       Everlasting Father, Prince of Peace.

(ISAIAH 9:2, 6)

The prophet Isaiah was among the first to portray the anticipated Christ as light. Throughout the Gospels light is used to illustrate that the radiance of God has come into a dark world and the darkness has not put it out. The first book of the Bible, Genesis, tells us that in the beginning the earth was without form and void; and there was only darkness until at God's word light was created. Revelation, the final book of the Bible, reports that "the city does not need the sun or the moon to shine on it, for the glory of God gives it light, and the Lamb is its lamp" (Revelation 21:23).

Although the religious significance of light has been observed in many ancient cultures, it is particularly so in Christian imagery. With the celebration of the birth of Jesus taking place during the dim, short days of December, Christmas brings renewed hope to a world lost in darkness by pointing to Jesus as "the Dayspring," "the Morning Star," and "the Light of the World."

Many lovely narratives have been derived from Matthew's brief account of the Christmas star. It's a story that has been told in various forms all over the world. Here are two of them.

The Brightest Star of All

After the birth of the Christ Child, the stars began to argue among themselves over who they believed God should choose to lead the wise men to Jesus. The great Sirius thought the Lord should choose him because he shone brighter than any other star; Mizar, as a double star, thought that he would be selected; while Alpha Scorpii, the star with the greatest magnitude, believed the honor would go to him. During these discussions Polaris, the great North Star, said nothing, as it was quite obvious to him who indeed was most qualified and most likely to be chosen.

So the magnificent and powerful stars continued to debate their qualifications. Only the little star Stella was quiet. She was too shy even to think of joining the conversation, as she knew she was neither great nor bright. But Stella was happy to serve as a small and insignificant little star, since that was the way God had made her.

Various other stars, because they also were big or bright or prominent, claimed the right to be selected. But God, who knows the hearts of all, decided to choose small and modest Stella. At that moment, the diminutive Stella, that humble point of light, burst into flaming brilliance. Seeing her beams, the wise men followed them to the manger where the Holy Infant lay. Today, everyone knows Stella as the brightest star of all.

The Light in the Well

The Bethlehem star was tired. She had made a long journey, guiding the wise men to the Holy Infant. As the exhausted star finished her trip, without knowing quite how it happened, she accidentally fell into a well near the place where the baby lay sleeping.

19

"Oh, my," said the star, who had used up all her strength in traveling, "whatever will I do?"

The other stars, hearing her, reached down their beams and pulled the Bethlehem star back into the heavens, where she shone brilliantly once again. But to this day, when you peer down into a well at night, if you have a pure heart you will see the radiance of the Bethlehem star still shining at the bottom of the well.

♦ ♦ ♦ ♦

In many countries, the Christmas celebration begins with the sighting of the first star on Christmas Eve. This Christmas star both declares the birth of Jesus and symbolizes the hopes of humanity for God's will to reign on earth as it did the night Christ was born. When we think of our God who counts the millions of stars and calls each by name, how logical it is that God would choose a star to direct the first worshipers to his Son.

Those stars of more than two thousand years ago are the same stars we see today. Whatever barriers keep people apart on earth, all of us share the stars and their beauty. Just as the wise men were guided to the Christ Child by the light of a single star, we too can follow Jesus, "the Bright and Morning Star," and let his light be reflected in our lives.

In Europe, stories of the wise men following the Bethlehem star sometimes include the characters of Babushka and La Befana. Both are grandmotherly figures who are more concerned with their own affairs and comfort than with accompanying the wise men. Babushka appears in folktales of Poland, Russia, and the Ukraine; whereas in Italy, the story of La Befana is known throughout the land.

Babushka

Babushka, a kind old lady who lived alone in a small hut, spent a lot of time keeping everything neat and orderly in her modest home. One day the three wise men stopped by on their way to Bethlehem. They asked for a drink, and Babushka poured each of them a glass of sparkling cold water.

"Come with us, Babushka," said one of the wise men. And the other two quickly added, "Yes, come with us to worship the Holy Infant at Bethlehem."

"But it is so cold outside," answered Babushka, "and I have not yet finished dusting my little hut."

Hearing that, the wise men went on their way. But they had no sooner moved out of sight than Babushka realized she had made a mistake.

She lamented, "I should have gone to see the wondrous child."

Hoping to catch up with them, Babushka filled a basket of presents to take to the baby and hurried out looking for the travelers. But snow had fallen, obscuring their path, and Babushka never found them.

To this day she travels the world looking for the Holy Infant. And along the way, she leaves gifts for children in remembrance of the Christ Child.

La Befana

High in the mountains of Italy, there lived the good witch called La Befana. When the wise men came to visit her, they invited her to travel with them as they followed the heavenly star to Bethlehem. But La Befana was so busy cleaning her small hut that she refused.

La Befana continued sweeping away with her big black broomstick, and the strangers went on their way. Just a little later, though, La Befana began to feel sorry that she had not gone with the wise men to pay her respects to the child. Seeing the bright light in the sky, she decided to follow the star and catch up with the travelers.

Quickly La Befana packed a big bag full of presents for the baby, then threw a shawl over her shoulders, jumped on her broomstick, and set out to find her way to the wise men. But La Befana could not find the guiding light again.

Every year, the rather ugly but kindly old witch can be

seen on her broomstick flying through the skies, searching for the bright star to show her the way to Bethlehem. La Befana continues her search to this day, and along the way she distributes her gifts to the children of Italy. If a child has not been good, La Befana leaves only a piece of coal as a warning to the child to be better in the future.

♦ ♦ ♦ ♦

Delightful as the stories of La Befana and Babushka are, they also serve as cautionary tales. How often do busy schedules or concern for our own comfort keep us from paying homage to the Child of Bethlehem? Throughout the Bible the importance and the brevity of time are indicated again and again. The writer of Ecclesiastes emphatically warns, "No man knows when his hour will come" (Ecclesiastes 9:12).

Jesus too spoke of the boundaries of time and the need to take action while there is still time. He warned that eventually a day would arrive when "you will look for me, but you will not find me" (John 7:34; 12:35). Unlike Babushka and La Befana, we must not hesitate. Jesus is inviting us to come to him now; indeed, let us seek the Christ Child today.

One of the most charming Christmas traditions connected with light is the custom of putting a candle in the window. This practice recognizes the search of Mary and Joseph for a place to stay in Bethlehem and the fact that there was no room for them at the inn. Some versions of the tradition call for a candle to be placed in the window to guide Mary and Joseph to a home that will welcome them. In other versions, the candle is put in the window to guide the actual Christ Child as he wanders from house to house looking for a place to stay.

Saint Jerome wrote that the lighting of candles was a means of expressing Christian joy over the baby who was born to bring enlightenment to a dark and suffering world. In candles we see a symbol of Christ, with the flame representing his divine or spiritual nature and the wax symbolizing his human nature.

Candles on the Advent wreath are another way in which we can rekindle the light of Christ in our homes. The circular form of the wreath, with no beginning and no end, signifies the eternity of God, while the evergreens denote the immortality of the soul and the life everlasting offered by Christ. The four candles represent the four weeks before Christmas, when the entire season is filled with anticipation and reflection. The first candle stands for prayer. The second represents hope. The third is known as the candle of joy, and the fourth as the candle of love. In the center is the Christ candle, which is lit on Christmas Eve to remind us to make Jesus, the Light of the World, the center and focus of our lives.

An appealing custom observed by many churches is the Christmas Eve candlelight service, which ends with the priest or minister lighting a candle from the Christ candle or altar candle. That flame is passed to the candles of those helping with the service, who in turn pass it to the candles of the waiting congregation, row by row, until the entire church is brilliant with light.

Family and Group Activities

1. Start and end each gathering with a simple prayer for understanding, faith, and an increase in our love for the Baby of Bethlehem.

2. Between Thanksgiving and Christmas Eve establish a tradition of sharing by selecting a family or group member to read a story. Because the narratives follow the Nativity story chronologically, they can be read consecutively; or, since each short story is complete in itself, they can be enjoyed in any order. Select a different family member or group member to read at each gathering.

3. Incorporate one or more of the stories into an Advent service. Since these are stories about light, they would appropriately fit into an Advent candle-lighting service.

Craft Suggestions

1. Make an Advent wreath. You can purchase a circular foam base with four candle holes, or you can use a large, round, flat dinner plate. With a lit candle, allow melted wax to fall on four equidistant spots around the outside of the plate. While the wax is still warm, place one rose candle and three purple candles in the melted wax. (Traditionally purple is the color of preparation, penance, and royalty; and rose represents joy.) As the wax hardens, it will hold the candles in place. Do the same for a larger white Christ candle in the center. After the candles are in place, add some evergreen branches between the candles to form a ring and complete the wreath. Many churches provide leaflets describing Advent services for home use, or families and groups may want to write their own services with a prayer, a Bible reading, and the recitation or singing of a favorite carol.

2. Create a paper-chain Advent calendar. Cut a series of half-inch by six-inch strips from red and green construction paper, enough so there will be one strip for each day of Advent. Make loops from the paper strips and link them together using glue or staples. Attach the final link to a star cut from the same material and decorated with glitter if available. Attach a string to the back of the star so it can be hung on a doorknob or over the mantel. Then,

during Advent, the family or group can remove one link per day, until on Christmas Day only the star remains to remind us that Jesus is the Light of the World. This paper-chain calendar makes a simple craft for the youngest children. Older children can supplement the activity by writing names for Jesus on the inside surfaces of the loops, then reflecting on each name as they remove that link. Some favorite names and titles of Jesus are: Almighty (Revelation 1:8), Alpha and Omega (Revelation 1:8; 22:13), Author of Life (Acts 3:15), Bread of God (John 6:33), Bread of Life (John 6:35; 6:48), Bridegroom (Matthew 9:15), Chief Cornerstone (Ephesians 2:20), Gate (John 10:9), Good Shepherd (John 10:11, 14), Holy and Righteous One (Acts 3:14), Immanuel (Matthew 1:23), King of Kings (1 Timothy 6:15; Revelation 19:16), Lamb of God (John 1:29), Light of the World (John 8:12), Lord of All (Acts 10:36), Mighty God (Isaiah 9:6), Morning Star (Revelation 22:16), Rock (1 Corinthians 10:4), Savior (Ephesians 5:23; 2 Peter 2:20), Son of God (John 1:49; Hebrews 4:14), Son of Man (Matthew 8:20), True Vine (John 15:1), Truth (John 14:6), Way (John 14:6), Wisdom of God (1 Corinthians 1:24), Word of God (Revelation 19:13).

CHAPTER TWO

Animal Stories

The many animals featured in the Bible show us the importance of all God's creatures. God created animals to benefit humanity, and the imagery and symbolism of animals help us understand the wisdom and morality of divine teachings. From Genesis, the first book of the Bible, where we read that God created every living creature "and saw that it was good," through the animals of Revelation, the last book of the Bible, there is much to be learned from the animal kingdom.

The prophet Isaiah foretold the new realm of love and harmony that the birth of Jesus would bring into the world—the "peaceable kingdom," where

The wolf will live with the lamb, / the leopard will lie down with the goat, / the calf and the lion and the yearling together; / and a little child will lead them.... They will neither harm nor destroy / on all my holy mountain, / for the earth will be full of the knowledge of the LORD, / as the waters cover the sea. (Isaiah 11:6, 9)

When Jesus arrived, he was born in a stable, and so lowly animals were the first to see and welcome the Holy Infant. The greatest artists and the earliest paintings of the birth of Christ have depicted animals in the stable along with the shepherds and the Magi. Ever since Saint Francis set up the first crèche in the thirteenth century, representing the birth of Jesus, animals have been an essential part of Nativity scenes. One can hardly imagine a manger setting without the presence of animals paying homage to the Christ Child. The lowly beasts were included to demonstrate that all creation recognized and loved the baby Jesus as their divine sovereign.

There are numerous stories of animals that were involved in the birth of Christ. Originating in the folklore of Europe is the belief that Christ was born at the stroke of midnight. At that hour on Christmas Eve, animals all over the world are thought to take on human characteristics and are given the power to speak.

One story tells of a rooster crowing at midnight to announce the birth of Jesus to the world so that all creation would be filled with joy and take part in appreciating the gift of the Divine Child.

Rooster's Proclamation

On the beautiful, starry night when Jesus was born, Rooster flew to the rooftop and proclaimed to the entire world: "Christ is born!"

Raven asked: "When?"

Crow answered: "This very night."

Ox cried: "Where, where?"

Sheep replied: "Bethlehem."

Goat declared: "Let us go see the Christ Child."

Hen repeated: "Yes, we must go there at once!"

And all the animals went to Bethlehem to welcome the newborn King. They bowed their heads to let the little baby know that they loved and worshiped him.

◆ ◆ ◆ ◆

The idea that the animal kingdom and all nature shared in the birth of Christ may seem odd to us today, but when we recall that God is the Lord of all creation, the idea becomes more wonderful than eccentric. In recognition of the belief that animals greeted Jesus at the hour of his birth, many people believe that at midnight on Christmas Eve, animals not only are given the power to speak but also bow their heads and sing praises to the Child of Bethlehem. Psalm 148 specifically calls on all nature and all humanity to praise the Lord:

Praise him, sun and moon,
  praise him, all you shining stars...
you mountains and all hills,
  fruit trees and all cedars,
wild animals and all cattle,
  small creatures and flying birds...
young men and maidens,
  old men, and children....
Praise the LORD. (3, 9-10, 12, 14)

The Camel's Hump

Three wise men in the East saw the Christ star and set out to worship the newborn King. In order to reach Bethlehem, the caravan had to cross hundreds of miles of desert. But in their rush to reach the baby before the great star disappeared, the wise men neglected to carry enough water for themselves and the camels.

When they realized their mistake, the wise men asked the camels, "Can you go without rest and water until we reach Bethlehem?" Being eager to worship the little King, the camels quickly agreed. Disregarding their thirst and their aching legs, the camels hurried across the long desert miles. When they finally reached the stable, the camels fell on their knees, worshiping the holy baby and giving thanks to God for enabling them to make the trip without rest or water.

To thank the loyal camels, God rewarded them with

great humps in which to store water for long trips. And to this day, riders mount their camels only after the faithful animals have bent their knees in an attitude of prayer.

The Ox and the Donkey

Many years ago in a stable in Bethlehem, there lived two animals, Ox and Donkey. Even though Ox was three times the size of Donkey, and Donkey could never be as strong as Ox, they came to be great friends. Their days were spent working hard, and in the evening they discussed the day's activities and rested together.

One evening a young couple named Mary and Joseph came to the stable, and later that night, in a manger, Mary gave birth to a baby named Jesus. Shepherds came to visit the baby, and as they knelt before the manger, Donkey edged closer to see the baby for himself. Ox wanted to do the same but was afraid that his long horns might frighten the little one, so he stayed back, sad that he had nothing to offer the child.

As Ox stood there, his breath drifted across the stable, gently warming the sleeping child. The baby stirred and woke up. Opening his eyes, the baby looked up at Donkey and smiled at Ox across the stable. In that moment Ox and Donkey were filled with the warmth of Christmas. From that day forth they carried it with them wherever they went.

The Donkey with a Thorn in His Hoof

Following the decree of Caesar Augustus that a census must be taken, a man named Joseph asked Mary, who was engaged to him, to travel with him to Bethlehem in order to register. Gently, as she was large with child, Joseph placed Mary on his small donkey, and they set off.

On the first night of the journey, the little donkey stepped on a thorn. The thorn was so painful that within a few hours the donkey was walking with a limp. However, knowing how important it was to get to Bethlehem, the faithful animal carried on in spite of the pain, safely delivering Mary to the stable where a short time later the child was born.

That night an angel visited the tired little donkey, telling him that later the donkey would carry that same baby, as a grown man, into Jerusalem to give his life for others. Hearing this news made the donkey proud but sad. The angel said, "Because you have quietly accepted pain without complaint, from now on all of your kind will carry a tear in their eye as a sign of your faithfulness."

To this day, donkeys have a look of sorrow about them, in memory of the little donkey's painful trip to Bethlehem, his sad journey into Jerusalem, and his loyalty to the man who twice rode on his back.

The Boy Who Was Blind and the Bell

When the shepherds heard the angels' message about the birth of Jesus, they hurried to Bethlehem, telling the news to everyone as they traveled. Soon a crowd started following the shepherds, as they too wanted to see the miraculous baby lying in a manger.

Along the way, a boy who was blind sat beside the road. Hearing the travelers, he begged them to take him along, but no one would stop to help him. Sorrowfully, he heard the crowd pass by, and the night grew silent again.

Then, in the distance, he heard the sound of a cowbell. Slowly, one step at a time, he followed the sound of the bell to a stable. There someone took his hand and led him inside, where, along with the cowbell, he heard the sounds of a baby. He had found the Christ Child. Kneeling in prayer, the boy thanked God for the wonderful gift of the newborn King and added a special thanks for the cow and her bell that had led him to the stable.

From that time onward, the musical chimes of bells, whether great or small, in churches or on cows, have always been associated with leading worshipers to Jesus.

♦ ♦ ♦ ♦

During the Middle Ages, people wrote books known as *bestiaries*, with words and pictures of animals and birds. Following the description of each beast, with its particular attributes and symbolic qualities, was a story with a moral or religious lesson. These books reflected the belief that the entire physical world is literally the word of God and that every living thing has its own instructive meaning. The peacock, for instance, stands for immortality and reminds us of the resurrection of Jesus. The ox, as a beast of burden, and the donkey, the most humble of animals, are frequently included in Nativity scenes to demonstrate that not only great kings or wise men came to pay homage to the Christ Child, but that the lowly animals also worshiped the Holy Infant.

In his birth and throughout his life, Jesus is identified with animals and is symbolically known both as the "Lamb of God" and the "Lion of Judah." In Christian imagery the lamb suggests innocence and sacrifice, whereas the lion is a very old symbol of the Resurrection signifying the strength and protection of God. Christ's close connection with animals visibly demonstrates that the animal kingdom shares in the eternal salvation that his birth brought to the world. It is comforting to realize that oxen, sheep, donkeys, and all creatures are included in God's amazing love and care.

Family and Group Activities

1. As a family or group, visit an animal shelter and make a donation.

2. Using two or three of the legends in this book, put on a family or group Christmas play for friends, neighbors, and other groups, or as part of a church service or neighborhood gathering. Ask a narrator to read the legend while other participants pantomime the action. Groups and individuals also can create and produce their own sketches from the stories by writing scripts in their own words. Any of these activities can be developed as an intergenerational project, since people of all ages enjoy performing.

Craft Suggestion

Construct a crèche. Make your own clay by mixing together 4 cups of flour, 1 cup of salt, and 1¾ cups of water, and then invite participants to create people and animals out of the clay. When the figures are complete, dry them for about three hours in a 200-degree oven. Once dried, the figures can be painted with poster or tempera paint. Even if the results are less than perfect, this activity is sure to generate laughter and build memories.

CHAPTER THREE

Bird Stories

In Christian thought, birds often represent the presence of God. We have the familiar image of the Holy Spirit descending like a dove on Jesus at the time of his baptism. The eagle, referred to in numerous Bible passages, represents both power and new life; in caring for its young, the eagle presents a vivid illustration of God's love. The robin, arriving in the spring, stands for a new beginning and denotes God's ability to renew life.

Jesus often referred to birds, speaking of a sparrow, dove, and raven. In the Sermon on the Mount he emphasized God's love and care for us by comparing our value to God with the heavenly Father's tender concern for the birds of the air (Matthew 6:26).

In all these images and descriptions of birds, we are challenged to learn something of God's love for all creation and the beauty of God's universal design.

Birds appear in Christmas stories as well, as we can see from the following narratives.

The Owl

On the night when Jesus was born, Rooster flew to the rooftop and proclaimed to the entire world: "Christ is born!" The animals heard him and wanted to go to Jerusalem to pay homage to the Infant King. But Owl, a curious old bird, wanted to know more about the baby before he would agree to participate. Boldly, with an almost superior air, Owl demanded of Rooster, "Who? Who is this Savior? Who? Who?"

Patiently Rooster explained about the baby Jesus, and then invited Owl to come with them to Jerusalem. Still Owl hesitated. It would be a long trip, and who was this baby king, anyway? Finally the animals could wait no longer. They set off for Jerusalem, leaving Owl behind. And that was how Owl missed his chance to greet the baby Jesus.

To this day, Owl recognizes the mistake he made and acknowledges his error by continuing to ask, "Who? Who?"

The Wren and the Robin

On the night when Christ was born, Wren and Robin went to the stable along with the other animals. Seeing the baby shiver in the cold night, the two birds knew they had to do something to help warm the baby.

Wren flew all about the stable, finding soft new moss. Working tirelessly through the night, the little bird put all the bits of moss together to make a warm cover for the sleeping child.

Robin, a plain bird without any special plumage or colors, swooped down and fanned the dying embers of the fire. Beating her wings rapidly, Robin soon had the fire glowing with flames that warmed the cold stable. Robin was so busy fanning the flames she didn't notice that her breast had been scorched.

Since that night, Wren's kindness has always been remembered. And forever after, Robin's breast has been red, a reminder of loving help given on the night that Jesus was born.

♦ ♦ ♦ ♦

Birds soaring into the heavens are often compared to human prayers that rise upward to God. In the Christmas stories about birds we are reminded that, like Owl, we can disregard the Infant King; or, like Wren and Robin, we can bring Jesus our contributions of service and love, knowing that even the smallest prayer can be answered.

Family and Group Activities

1. Encourage each person in your family or group to create a prayer as though they were one of the small birds in this section. For example, write Robin's or Owl's prayer.
2. Following the examples of Wren and Robin, find a way this week to do a small service or kindness for someone else.

Craft Suggestion

Make a simple bird feeder by covering a pine cone with peanut butter, pressing birdseed into it, and then using string to hang the cone from a tree branch or shrub.

CHAPTER FOUR

Stories About Spiders and Insects

T he writer of Proverbs points out: "Four things on earth are small, yet they are exceedingly wise" (30:24 NRSV). Creatures listed as having remarkable characteristics of persistence and discipline are ants, badgers, locusts, and lizards. In the Bible and in life, seemingly insignificant creatures sometimes play important roles. Bees and ants provide wonderful models of industry, and we have much to learn from other small creatures as well. Even the smallest life-form in the Bible serves as a mirror to display the beauty and providence of the Divine Creator.

After Jesus' birth, the Holy Family fled to Egypt to escape Herod's soldiers, who were searching for the newborn King in order to kill him and eliminate the threat he posed to the authority of Herod. The family's journey gave rise to several stories telling of a spider that helped hide the Holy Child. Spiders and insects have also made appearances in other Christmas stories.

The Christmas Spider

After Jesus was born, an angel of the Lord warned Joseph to escape from Herod by going to Egypt with the Holy Infant. Following miles of travel, the weary family took refuge in a cave along the roadside. As they settled in for the night, Joseph heard a noise outside. It was Herod's soldiers, searching for them. Desperate to protect his family, Joseph tried to move a great boulder to cover the cave entrance, but he didn't have the strength to lift it.

High above, a spider watched Joseph struggle. Recognizing the danger to the baby, the spider left her comfortable corner and began working as fast as she could, spinning a web across the entrance. When the soldiers arrived, one started to enter the cave, but was told by another, "Don't bother wasting time there. You can see from the spiderweb that no one has entered the cave." The soldiers went on their way, and the baby was saved by the spider's quick action.

Ever since, to commemorate the spider's gift, people have decorated their Christmas trees with silvery, shimmering threads to represent the spider's web.

The Spider and the Christmas Tree

Long ago, in a small town in Germany, there lived a kindly old woman. As Christmas approached, the woman cleaned out a special corner of her house to make room for a Christmas tree. In her cleaning, the woman came across a spiderweb tucked up in the corner. She started to sweep away the web, but then she noticed a tiny spider trembling in the center.

"It's all right," she told the spider. "I won't hurt you." She left the spider and his web just as she had found them.

When the woman finished cleaning, she went into the forest and brought back a lovely tree, placing it in her special corner. But the woman was so poor that she couldn't afford to buy decorations for the tree. Even so, she thought the bare branches were beautiful the way they seemed to be reaching up to heaven to honor the Child of Bethlehem.

Above the tree, the spider watched and waited. When the woman went to bed on Christmas Eve, he climbed down to the tree and started to work.

On Christmas morning, the woman got up and went to admire her tree. She was amazed to find it draped with glittering silver garlands! Examining them more closely, she realized that the garlands were intricately woven spiderwebs.

The woman looked up into the corner and saw the spider, illuminated by the sun in the center of his web. He had returned kindness with kindness, weaving his Christmas wishes into the tree.

"Merry Christmas," said the woman. And so it was.

The Gift of the Spider

Most of the animals that came to Bethlehem to see the Holy Child brought gifts for the baby. But there was one little spider in the group that didn't have anything to give the child.

"Maybe I can spin a web for him," the spider thought, and she set about covering a tree branch at the front of the stable. When the web was finished, it was dull and gray. The little spider was disappointed because she had hoped to make something beautiful for the baby.

The spider slept fitfully that night, worried about her gift. When she awoke, the sun was shining, and something at the front of the stable was glowing. It was the web! During the night dewdrops had settled on it, and the morning sun lit it up like a string of glistening beads.

The Christ Child smiled at the pretty sight, and in that moment the little spider knew that her simple gift was appreciated.

The Beetle

In the town of Bethlehem, high up in the stable where Jesus was born, lived a small insect named Beetle. Filled with joy at the baby's birth, Beetle flew from the stable to tell his friends, the bugs and insects, and bring them back to worship the Holy Child.

While searching for his insect friends, Beetle met a group of angels, who were proclaiming: "Glory to God in the highest, and on earth peace, goodwill toward men." One of the angels, pleased with Beetle's wish to tell others of God's precious gift, plucked a star from the sky and delicately placed it on Beetle's back.

When at last Beetle found his insect friends, they were amazed to see the sparkling light on his back. "Let's give Beetle a new name in honor of his flashing light," cried one little bug.

"Yes, yes," chorused the others, "that's a good idea."

"Let's name him Firefly," suggested the wise old Daddy Longlegs.

The other insects agreed. And from that time on, wherever Firefly went, his brightly blinking light reminded all creation of his desire to tell others about God's great gift of the baby Jesus, the "Light of the World."

♦ ♦ ♦ ♦

Such modest stories of humble insects remind us that even the most insignificant creature giving the smallest service to God is of value. We don't have to be rich to bring a gift to Jesus; like the little firefly, it is sufficient to want to share his story with others. The insects in these simple stories teach us the value of everything in existence—to serve a purpose in life and also to join with us in adoration of the Christ Child. The Bible clearly reveals that in the new City of God, "every creature in heaven and on earth and under the earth and in the sea, and all that is in them" will join with the human family in adoring and worshiping our creator (Revelation 5:13 NRSV).

Like the small insects in these stories, we can do no better than be guided by the words of Christina Rossetti:

> What can I give Him, poor as I am?
> If I were a shepherd, I would bring a
>   lamb;
> If I were a Wise Man, I would do my
>   part;
> Yet what I can I give Him—Give my
>   heart.

Family and Group Activities

1. Following the example of Firefly, tell someone about Jesus. Invite a friend to church or to a special Christmas service.

2. Should you happen to meet a spider one day, remember the old English nursery rhyme: "If you wish to live and thrive / Let a spider run alive."

Craft Suggestion

In many parts of the world, the spider is a symbol of good luck. The house spider especially is thought to bring good fortune to the inhabitants of the home where the spider lives. In Germany, where the story of the Christmas-tree spider is believed to have originated, it is customary to make a "good luck spider" and place it among the tinsel webs on the tree. This simple spider ornament can be made with a black pom-pom and black pipe cleaners. Both are available in craft stores. Simply glue four one-inch pipe-cleaner legs on two sides of the pom-pom, and add a string for hanging. An even simpler spider can be cut from black construction paper or from a child's drawing and placed on the tree.

CHAPTER FIVE

Plant
Stories

Some of the most charming stories about the birth of Christ involve plants and the natural world. In fact, the word *nature* derives from the Latin *natura* or *nasci,* which means birth. That nature itself should originate from the word for the beginning of life is consistent with our understanding of God as the creator of all life and all nature. This etymological relationship between the words *nature* and *birth* continues in the "Nativity" or birth of Christ.

As we also saw with animals, plants and the scenery of the natural world are referred to frequently in the Bible. From the prophet Isaiah's description of Christ himself as a tender plant to the joy of the wilderness at his birth, the idea of all creation seeing the glory of the Lord is acknowledged.

Francis of Assisi, who developed the first Christmas crèche in the thirteenth century, commented on the relationship among the various parts of the natural world and expressed the idea that all creation mirrors the hand of its Creator. He spoke of Brother Sun, Sister Moon and the stars, Brother Air, and Sister Water, and ended his famous blessing, "Canticle of the Creatures," with a plea to God: "Teach us to see your design in all of Creation."

Perhaps today we are too sophisticated to think of plants singing and deserts blossoming in exultation at Christ's birth, but in an earlier age such miraculous happenings were widely believed. Early European folklore expressed the conviction that plants and trees growing along the banks of the Jordan River bowed in the direction of Bethlehem on the night that Christ was born. Later additions to the stories taught that on every Christmas Eve to this day, vegetation throughout the world continues to show reverence by bowing down in this way.

The Rosemary Bush

When Mary washed the garments of the baby Jesus, she looked about for a place where she could hang them to dry. Palm and Sugarcane both clamored for the honor, arguing about who could be most helpful to the Holy Family by holding the infant's clothes.

Palm said, "I give shelter during the heat of the day."

Sugarcane replied, "I provide sweetness and make a refreshing drink."

Off to the side, poor little Rosemary listened to their argument. She wanted to offer something special too but thought she was just a dull little bush. And so she remained silent.

Mary asked Palm to bend down so that she might hang Jesus' clothes on a branch, but try as he might, the tall Palm could not bend low enough.

Sugarcane called, "Me, me!" But when she leaned forward the clothes slid off her straight, slippery stems.

Then Mary noticed a humble bush nearby. It was Rosemary. "Perfect," thought Mary, and gently laid the clothes on Rosemary's low, spreading branches.

At that moment, modest little Rosemary sprouted lovely blue flowers, the color of the Virgin's gown. And they have remained to this day, in recognition of Rosemary's usefulness and her sweet, unpretentious nature.

♦ ♦ ♦ ♦

The delicate blue flowers given to the rosemary bush remind us of the blue of the Virgin's cloak. Religious art almost always depicts Mary wearing blue, as the color signifies Mary's quality of innocent devotion. Blue, the color of the clear sky, also signifies truth and thoughtfulness. Just as her blue cloak of love enfolds the mother of Jesus, we too can wrap a mantle of adoration about ourselves, helping us remember the humility and dedication of the rosemary bush.

One of the best-known plants associated with Christmas is the brilliant green holly bush. However, it was not always that color. Both of the following stories explain changes in the color of the holly bush.

The Holly Plant

Joseph and Mary took the baby Jesus to Egypt to escape the wrath of Herod. On the way, they stopped to rest along the roadside. As they were about to start on their way again, they heard Herod's soldiers coming after them. They looked about for a place to hide, but the desert afforded no shelter. The only thing growing nearby was a dull, dry holly bush.

Seeing the family's plight, the holly bush opened its arms to offer protection. Gratefully, Joseph led Mary and the baby Jesus under the low, thick branches. One of the soldiers started toward the holly bush; but knowing the dull holly leaves to be pointed and sharp, he decided no one would try to hide there. The soldier turned back again and went on his way.

The holly bush saved Mary, Joseph, and Jesus. As a sign of gratitude, the Christ Child touched the dull, brown leaves, changing them to a rich emerald green. The holly bush remains green to this day, and it remains so throughout the year, in recognition of the loving help it gave to the Holy Family.

The Boy and the Holly Bush

When Jesus was born, the angels brought tidings of great joy to shepherds in the field. Among those shepherds, gazing in wonder, stood a little orphan boy.

The shepherds declared, "We must go immediately and see this miraculous baby," and they made preparations to leave.

"Please," begged the orphan boy, "let me come with you to honor the newborn King."

When the shepherds agreed, the boy was delighted. But in the next moment, sadness overcame him as he realized he had no gift to give the Holy Baby.

While the shepherds looked over the sheep to select the finest lamb for the Holy Child, the boy searched for something he could bring. The only thing he could find was a dull, brown holly bush with white berries. He immediately set to work weaving its branches into a crown for the little King.

The boy traveled to Bethlehem with the shepherds and found the baby. But when he laid his crown before the infant, the boy was so ashamed of his gift that he started to cry. The Holy Infant looked at the boy, reached out his little hand, and touched the wreath, turning its leaves a shimmering green and its berries crimson. They have remained that way to this day, reflecting the love of the orphan boy and the bright smile offered in return by the baby Jesus.

♦ ♦ ♦ ♦

The touch of Jesus in our lives can fill the dullest of days with bright, exhilarating hues. The great English poet William Blake wrote that the beauty and power of God's universal love can be found in even the smallest part of God's creation. In familiar lines, Blake tells us that if we would but look carefully, we will indeed be able

> to see the world in a grain of sand
> And a heaven in a wild flower,
> Hold Infinity in the palm of your hand
> And Eternity in an hour.

Decorating our homes with greenery, mistletoe, holly, ivy, pine, and fir is a tradition that dates back many centuries. An English carol from the fifteenth century tells of a contest between Holly and Ivy over who should be assigned the best place in the hall. Although both plants, being evergreens, were valued as symbols of immortality, tradition relates that Holly was given the place of honor because of her willing service in hiding the Holy Family on their way to Egypt.

In the contest between Holly and Ivy, one is reminded of the disciples' concern over a place of honor in the Lord's kingdom and the reply of Jesus. After describing how he came to serve others, Jesus identified loving service as the source of greatness: "The greatest among you will be your servant...and whoever humbles himself will be exalted" (Matthew 23:11-12).

Other stories involving plants relate this same desire to be of assistance. Two examples are stories of the sage plant and the bayberry bush giving shelter to the Holy Family while the Family was on their flight to Egypt. In all the stories, the plants' helpful acts of kindness result in divine gifts of appreciation.

Because the bayberry bush protected the little family during a storm, for example, it was rewarded by never having lighting strike it. And the sage plant was given authority to help remedy ills and increase wisdom, attributes still remembered today when the sage plant is used as a medication for colds and when the word *sage* is associated with wisdom.

Family and Group Activities

1. Give a gift of service. Some of the stories in this chapter grew out of the fact that the central character had no gift to bring to the Holy Infant and so gave service instead. Encourage children and group members to discover ways to give of themselves in the home and community. Develop a project for your family or group that involves the giving of service rather than material objects.

2. Give a gift of time by visiting a shut-in or offering to spend an hour with someone doing something of that person's choosing.

Craft Suggestion

Make napkin rings. A set of six pretty yet easy-to-make napkin rings can be made from green felt or construction paper. Cut strips of felt or paper that are one inch by nine inches. Folding the two ends of each strip together, cut the ends in the shape of a holly leaf. Add berries by gluing on groups of three red dots or drawing the dots with a marker. On one end, just below the holly leaf, cut a three-quarter-inch slit in the center of the strip. Slide the other end of the strip through the slit and place it over a napkin. The green ring looks lovely on white paper napkins. The napkin rings can be used for a family meal; they also provide a good way for school groups to prepare for a holiday coffee hour or community supper. Group leaders can also check with hospitals and nursing homes to see if children's donations of napkin rings for the Christmas meal would be welcome.

CHAPTER SIX

Flower Stories

The prophet Isaiah wrote: "Thirsty deserts will be glad: barren lands will celebrate and blossom with flowers. Deserts will bloom everywhere and sing joyful songs. They will be as majestic as Mount Lebanon, as glorious as Mount Carmel or Sharon Valley. Everyone will see the wonderful splendor of the LORD our God" (Isaiah 35:1-2 CEV). The prophet continued speaking of the time when God's Son will come to save humanity, that joyous time when the desert will flow with fountains, when the people the Lord has rescued will sing and celebrate because all sorrows and worries will be gone (Isaiah 35).

Echoing Isaiah's thought, in the Song of Solomon the Bride says, "I am a rose of Sharon, a lily of the valleys"

(2:1 NRSV). In the New Testament, Christ is called the bridegroom and the church is the bride, completing the analogy of the love of Christ as the rose of Sharon. Since the rose is considered the most perfect of flowers, traditionally it has become an image of the perfect love of Jesus for all humanity and a symbol of the perfection of Jesus himself. The following stories of vivacious flowers reveal the interrelatedness of all created things and the certainty that everything in the universe is serving the purpose for which it was made.

The Christmas Rose

At the time Jesus was born in Bethlehem, a poor little shepherd girl named Madelon watched the wise men from the East bring their gifts of gold, frankincense, and myrrh to the Christ Child. She also saw the other shepherds bring their gifts of fruit and honey and wished that she had something precious to take to the baby.

As Madelon tended her sheep, gentle tears fell from her eyes because she had no gift to bring. "If only it were summer, I could pick a flower," Madelon thought sadly. An angel who was watching, moved by the sight of the poor little girl, changed each of Madelon's tears of love into a beautiful white rose. Madelon gathered up the flowers and ran to present them to the Christ Child. When his little hands touched the white petals, a delicate pink became perceptible. From then on, the graceful pink and white Christmas rose continues to bloom during the cold winter months and remains a symbol of faith and devotion.

♦ ♦ ♦ ♦

The Christmas rose is also known as the snow rose or the winter rose, because it blooms from late fall until early spring, when everything else is frozen. Christ as a rose is a theme found both in the Bible and in tradition. An unknown German author from the fifteenth century wrote this poem titled "Es ist ein Ros' Entsprungen":

> A Rose has sprung from a tender root,
> From Jesse, as those of old have sung,
> And it bore a flower,
> In the middle of a cold winter,
>
> When half spent was the night.
> Isaiah foretold it, the Rose I have in
>   mind;
> Is Mary the pure, the little flower has
>   brought us.
> From God's eternal wisdom, she bore a
>   child,
> And remained pure.

> The Flower, so small, whose sweet fra-
>   grance fills the air,
> Dispels with glorious splendor the dark-
>   ness everywhere;
> True man and truer God, helps us out of
>   all sorrows,
> Saves from sin and death.
>
> Oh Jesus, until we leave this misery,
> Let your help guide us into joy,
> In Your Father's Kingdom,
> Where we eternally praise you.
> Oh, God, allow us this.

It is said that the five pink and white petals of the Christmas rose call us to innocence, humility, gratitude, faith, and joy—attributes we must strive for if we would love Jesus. Traditionally, the Christmas rose is placed near the front door on Christmas Eve to greet the Christ Child.

Similar to the story of the Christmas rose is a legend from Mexico telling of a boy named Mario and how the poinsettia flower came into being.

The Poinsettia

Long ago in the high mountain village where Mario lived, the custom on Christmas Eve was for everyone to take flowers to church to give Jesus. But Mario was so poor that he had no money to purchase a flower for the beloved baby.

Walking slowly to church that Christmas Eve, Mario hoped he could find a wildflower to give the Christ Child. He searched carefully along the roadside but found only weeds. Then, in the darkness, he heard a gentle voice calling to him.

"Mario, pick the weeds, and remember that anything given in love is precious." Obeying the voice, Mario picked the weeds and took them to church, where he placed them at the foot of the manger.

When the other children saw his gift, they made fun of it. But when they looked again, the weeds had turned into brilliant red flowers—the beautiful plant we know today as the poinsettia. Mario knew then that the voice had been right: it is love that makes a gift beautiful.

♦ ♦ ♦ ♦

In Mexico, the poinsettia plant is known as *la flor de la Noche Buena*—that is, the flower of the Holy Night. Another story of the poinsettia states that the star of Bethlehem, which led the wise men to the manger, shone so brilliantly that the earth responded by producing a flower that mirrored the beauty of the star. The flower's pointed leaf petals were star shaped and had smaller white petals and a golden star in the center. It is said that on the day when Jesus died, some of the plants turned their petals to red, symbolizing his blood, and some remained white, symbolizing the purity of his sacrifice.

The origin of the following story dates back to the first Christians, who were very poor. To honor Mary as the mother of Christ, statues of her holding the precious infant were placed alongside the roadways. Poor worshipers, who had no coins to offer, planted yellow and orange flowers instead. This was done as a result of an earlier story about the Holy Family on the flight to Egypt.

The Marigold

After Jesus was born, Joseph fled with Mary and the child to Egypt to escape Herod. Shortly after they set out, the family was accosted by a band of robbers. The robbers had heard about the gift of gold that the wise men had given Jesus and were hoping to become rich by stealing it.

The thieves grabbed Mary's purse and ran away, sure that it contained enough to make them wealthy. But when they opened the purse, instead of money, beautiful orange and yellow flowers fell out that were shaped like coins. The thieves were so angry they threw the flowers along the roadway, muttering to themselves. There, the lovely flowers took root and grew, pleasing everyone who passed by.

♦ ♦ ♦ ♦

Hearing the story, reverent worshipers continued to honor the mother of Jesus by planting "Mary's gold" around roadside shrines. Eventually Mary's gold became the marigold we know today, whose name still reminds us of the Virgin. The gold color represents Mary's willingness to give herself and her son over to God's plan in spite of the sorrow it would bring. The marigold is also known as the flower of grief, since dew gathers in the petals during the night and resembles tears trickling off in the morning. As William Shakespeare wrote in *The Winter's Tale*, "The Mary-gold, that goes to bed wi' th' sun, and with him rises, weeping."

The story of the humble marigold challenges us to strive for the same spirit of giving and desire to follow God's will that the flower illustrates in symbolizing the mother of Jesus.

Family and Group Activities

1. Choose a favorite story and reflect on its meaning. Set aside a special time and place to think about the

characters in the story. See if you can find a verse in the Bible that has something to do with the story.

2. Make cupcakes and frost with white icing. Decorate them with "poinsettia flowers" by dividing a red fruit roll into one-inch by half-inch rectangles and shaping these into petals by cutting the ends to a point. With a dab of icing, arrange six to eight overlapping petals on each cupcake and place three mini M&M yellow candies in the center. Spearmint gumdrop leaves that have been cut in half can be added but are not necessary. This simple arrangement makes a surprisingly realistic flower.

Craft Suggestion

Make your own window clings. Young children will enjoy "planting" a Christmas flower garden on the window or refrigerator. Cut pictures of flowers from recycled Christmas cards, back with double-sided sticky tape, and display as desired.

CHAPTER SEVEN

Stories About Christmas Traditions

A child can hardly think of Christmas without associating the holiday with Santa Claus, candy canes, and Christmas trees. Such secular traditions have become so much a part of Christmas that many Christians are concerned that its true significance may be obscured. However, behind some of these secular traditions are meanings and associations that point to a deeper reality. Rather than dismissing the stories and traditions entirely, it might be more rewarding to look for the central or fundamental truths that they hold.

Santa Claus or some version of him is found throughout the world. In Denmark he is known as the Juleman. England has Father Christmas. In France we find Père Noël. Our name for Saint Nicholas is thought to be derived from the Dutch Sinterklaas, a shortened version of Saint (Sinter) Nicolaas (Klaas). When the Dutch settled in America, Sinterklaas eventually became the anglicized Santa Claus.

All these are based on an actual Saint Nicholas, who was born in Asia Minor in the fourth century. He was a bishop in the early church who was known for his generosity and kindness to all. Saint Nicholas is said to have gone about by night secretly distributing gifts to the poor. The red suit he wears to this day is derived from the robes of the bishop.

Here is one of the earliest and best-known stories of Saint Nicholas, or Santa Claus.

Santa Claus

One day, Saint Nicholas heard about a poor family in town whose three daughters wished to marry but had no dowries. In those long-ago days, it was necessary for families to provide their daughters with a dowry or gift of money when they married; otherwise there would be no wedding.

Now, the three girls were lovely and good, and many a young man would have liked to marry them, but without a dowry their chances were slim. So Saint Nicholas decided to do something about it.

One night he slipped out of his house and secretly left three bags of gold at the house of the poor family. When the daughters awoke the next morning, they found the gold and were able to have dowries. This generous gift made it possible for the three young daughters to marry, and everyone was delighted.

♦ ♦ ♦ ♦

The tradition of Saint Nicholas as a secret gift-giver grew out of the warm kindness and generosity of the real-life bishop. His compassion and love for the young helped him evolve into the favorite of all children—the Santa Claus we know today. The familiar custom of hanging stockings by the fireplace originated with another version of the story in which Saint Nicholas gave gold to the three daughters.

The Christmas Stockings

Night after night, the three lovely but lonely daughters wished for a dowry so they might wed. But the daughters knew there was little chance of their wish coming true, as the family really was very poor. They were so poor that each daughter owned just one pair of stockings and had to wash them every night. As the girls washed the stockings, they talked to one another about their hopes and dreams, then hung the stockings over the fireplace to dry and went to bed.

Meanwhile, the good bishop who came to be known as Santa Claus had made up his mind to help these lovely girls. One cold winter night, Santa was traveling through the air on his white horse and stopped on the roof of the little hut where the poor family lived. Smiling with delight, Santa took three bags of gold from his sack and threw the gold down the chimney, where it landed in the stockings hanging by the fireplace.

The next morning, the girls were amazed and delighted to find their stockings full of gold. With dowries in place, weddings were soon planned for all three sisters, and the whole village was invited. Ever since, children have hung stockings by the fireplace at Christmas, hoping that they too will receive gifts.

◆ ◆ ◆ ◆

The white horse of this story eventually evolved into the reindeer used by today's Santa. This same narrative also launched the tradition of Santa arriving through the chimney and delivering gifts in stockings hung at the fireplace.

Whether we know him as the German Kriss Kringle,

the Russian Grandfather Frost, or our own Santa Claus, Saint Nicholas brings to all of us the same lesson: joy is found in giving. Although the origin of giving gifts is attributed to the wise men bringing offerings to the baby Jesus, Santa Claus has helped establish the tradition of gifts as expressions of love and friendship, of piety in the giving to those less fortunate, or as an expression of gratitude for a gift received.

That Christmas has become the ultimate festival of gift giving is much more than a commercial enterprise. Giving gifts at Christmastime is really an expression of gratitude for God's gift of the Christ Child to all humanity.

The Candy Cane

Long ago in Cologne Cathedral, one of the most beautiful churches in Germany, the choirmaster wondered how he could keep the children quiet through the long Christmas Eve service. They were good girls and boys, but they tended to grow impatient during the service. Finally, the choirmaster promised the children a stick of sugar candy as a reward for sitting so patiently during the long evening.

Later, reflecting on the plainness of the candy, the choirmaster thought it would be more meaningful if the stick were bent at the top to resemble a shepherd's crook, to remind the children that shepherds were the first to hear about the birth of the Holy Infant. The following year, the choirmaster persuaded a candy maker to bend the stick into the shape of a shepherd's staff. This bent stick or cane is what he then presented to the boys and girls in the cathedral to remind them of that original Christmas Eve when the shepherds in the field heard the angels and went to worship the newborn King.

Another Story of the Candy Cane

It is said that at the turn of the century, there was a candy maker in Indiana who developed the candy cane as we know it today. This candy maker designed the candy to tell the true story of Jesus, the baby who was given by God to save the world from sin.

The candy maker kept the shape of the shepherd's crook both to remind people of the shepherds watching their sheep the night Christ was born, and to recall that the baby Jesus was the "Good Shepherd" who would give his life for his sheep. Then the candy maker added symbolic details that would bring to mind the real sacrifice of Jesus. He added red stripes: three small ones to represent the stripes of the Roman soldiers who beat Jesus and by which we are healed, and a wider stripe representing the blood shed by Christ on the cross. The white foundation was kept to remember the purity of Jesus, while the hardness of the candy recalls Jesus as our rock of refuge.

♦ ♦ ♦ ♦

Whereas we may enjoy a candy cane simply as a Christmas treat, it is certain that the candy did have its beginnings in Christian tradition. The interpretations of the stripes, the colors, and the hardness of the candy cane given through the years have become widely accepted as meaningful symbols of the love and sacrifice of Jesus. Additional significance is found in the shape of the candy, which when turned upside down looks like the *J* in Jesus.

The following stories relate several different accounts of the Christmas tree's origins. As with the stories of Santa Claus, the first tale derives from an actual person.

Saint Boniface and the Pine Tree

One of the earliest English missionaries to spread the story of Christianity among the German pagans was Saint Boniface. One Christmas Eve, Saint Boniface gathered his local converts together to watch as he chopped down a great oak tree. The destruction of the tree held great significance for the Germans, as it had been under this tree that children had been sacrificed to the pagan gods.

As the tree fell, it crushed everything in its path except for a small pine. Saint Boniface interpreted the survival of the pine as a miracle and concluded that the evergreen sapling should be known as "the tree of the Christ Child."

Saint Boniface used the shape and color of the little tree to teach the truths of Christianity. "See how it points to heaven," he told the people. "Let it direct your hearts to God." He added, "See how it remains green through the winter, a symbol of the everlasting life that Jesus offers."

The one-time pagans, among the first converts to Christianity, were quick to accept the little pine as a symbol of their newfound faith in the Baby of Bethlehem.

The Angels and the Christmas Tree

One time long, long ago, three angels were sent to earth to find a tree that would represent the Christian virtues of faith, hope, and love. The angels searched long and hard, until finally, when they came upon a tall fir tree, they realized they had found what they were looking for.

The fir was indeed as great as faith, as high as hope, and as precious as love. As such, it was a fitting reminder of the Christ Child: his faith in his mission, his hope of redeeming humanity, and his sacrificial love that opened the gates of heaven to all.

The Woodcutter and the Christmas Tree

There once was a poor but kindly woodcutter who lived with his wife deep in the forest. One stormy Christmas Eve, they heard a gentle knocking at their door. Opening the door, they discovered a small, hungry child, and although they were very poor, the couple shared what they had with the child and gave him shelter for the night.

In the morning, they were awakened by the sound of an angelic choir singing praises to God. The child had disappeared, but outside their door was a beautiful evergreen tree glistening in the sunlight. Seeing the tree, the woodcutter and his wife were amazed to realize that their visitor had been the Christ Child. He had created the evergreen, the first Christmas tree, to thank them for their kindness and as a symbolic reminder of his love and promise of everlasting life.

Martin Luther's Christmas Tree

One cold Christmas Eve , the great Reformation leader Martin Luther was returning home after a long day of preaching across the countryside. His route took him through a forest, where, looking up through the branches, he was struck by the magnificent stars glimmering overhead.

Martin Luther was so taken with the view that he cut down a small fir tree and carried it home to share the experience with his family. To recreate the glimmering stars, Luther placed small candles on the branches, lit them, and called in his wife and children. Together they enjoyed the radiant sight of the first Christmas tree.

♦ ♦ ♦ ♦

The Christmas tree is the center of festivities in most homes, but, far more than simply a decoration or holiday tradition, the tree has come to represent a number of spiritual ideas. Its branches pointing toward heaven remind us to look for heavenly rather than earthly treasures. Its survival through the cold winter months is symbolic of patience as it waits for the coming of spring and renewal; and that survival also reminds us of our belief in immortality. The tree's vibrant green color and its association with tall evergreens make it symbolic of triumphant growth. In Christian symbolism, green stands for our hope of God's eternal care, our faith in the everlastingness of his love, and our growth in the Christian life.

Family and Group Activities

1. Be a secret Santa. At the beginning of Advent, put the names of everyone in the family or group into a basket. Then ask each person to select a name without disclosing who it is. Through the rest of the season, the secret Santa does nice things for the recipient, such as offering a ride to church, helping in some unexpected way, doing chores for the other person, or just being particularly kind and helpful. On or around Christmas Eve, the secret Santas are revealed with a small gift exchange.
2. To remind everyone that we are celebrating the birth of Jesus, tie a candy cane on each of your wrapped gifts.

Craft Suggestion

Make a refrigerator magnet. Cut a picture that is one or two inches square from a used Christmas card. The picture can be part of a manger scene, an animal, a flower, a figure, a decoration, a symbol, or any other Christmas image. Laminate the picture and glue a strip magnet on the back. Laminating sheets and magnets can be found in office supply and craft stores, but clear tape and strips cut from advertising or business card magnets work fine. These little magnets are nice to use as favors and also to slip in with your Christmas cards.

Stories Linking Christmas and Easter

Celebrated around the world, Christmas is richer in traditions and stories than any other holiday. Although Christmas is a time of joy and celebration, we must always remember that Jesus' birth is inexorably linked to his death. The baby born to be King of all humanity would within a few years die to save the world; the precious infant lying in the wooden manger would become the courageous young Savior hanging on the wooden cross; the joyous birth in the stable would culminate in the agony of the garden and of the Crucifixion.

Thankfully, the story does not end there. Rather, the Christmas angel's tidings that "a Savior has been born to you; he is Christ the Lord" (Luke 2:11) will be echoed in the Easter angel's triumphant cry at the empty tomb: "He is not here; he has risen, just as he said" (Matthew 28:6). Linking these two events is the loving, teaching, giving life of Jesus, the foundation and cornerstone of our faith.

Elements of the joyful Christmas stories concerning the birth of Jesus are carried over to the anguish of the Crucifixion. The Christ candle in the Advent wreath evolves into the Paschal candle of Easter, with both representing Jesus as the Light of the World. The rooster that crowed at midnight to proclaim the birth of the Holy Infant is much the same as the rooster whose crowing reveals Peter's betrayal, and whose continuing cry on the dawn of Easter Day announces that Christ is risen, light has triumphed over darkness, and good has won out over evil. In the folklore of Easter we again meet the donkey that carried Mary to Bethlehem, as we also meet the plants, animals, birds, and trees whose stories are part of both Christmas and Easter.

The following stories contain elements linking the Christmas and Easter seasons and have been passed down to us through the years.

The Donkey and the Cross

When Jesus prepared to enter Jerusalem on Palm Sunday, he decided to ride a donkey, that simple beast of burden. The donkey was proud that he had been chosen, just as he had been chosen years before by Joseph to take the mother of Jesus to Bethlehem.

The little donkey proudly carried Jesus through the streets of Jerusalem that Sunday. Later that week, his pride turned to grief as he watched Jesus climb the hill of Calvary.

At that moment, an angel appeared, saying, "Don't be sad, little donkey. What has happened was meant to be." The angel added, "While you have been grieving here, the shadow of the cross has fallen across your back. So that everyone will know of your devoted loyalty, that shadow of the cross will remain on your back for all time."

Ever since then, a cross-shaped mark has appeared on the backs of many donkeys as a symbol of their willingness to give loving service even when it is painful to do so.

The Robin

At the foot of Calvary, little Robin saw a crowd formed around a silent, sorrowful man who labored under the weight of a rough wooden cross. The man was prodded along by Roman soldiers who, to humiliate and scorn him, placed a mock crown of thorns on his brow.

Seeing how cruelly the thorns of the dreadful crown

were wounding the poor man, Robin swooped down and tugged at the largest thorn with her beak, pulling with all her strength until the thorn came out. As she did, a drop of blood fell on Robin's breast, turning it a bright crimson.

Today, Robin Redbreast, as she has come to be known, modestly wears the color in memory of the day she was able to help the Savior of the world.

The Aspen Tree

Long ago, when Mary, Joseph, and the Holy Infant were fleeing from Herod on their way to Egypt, they passed through a great forest filled with beautiful flowers and tall, stately trees. Recognizing the heavenly Infant, the flowers bent their delicate heads in reverence, and the trees bowed low—all but the proud Aspen. Scornfully, Aspen held his head high and refused even to look at the Infant King.

Later, after Jesus had left, Aspen began to regret his arrogance, and he shivered with remorse. Through the years his trembling shame continued, until, years later, Aspen was given a chance to be used as the wood of the cross. He thought, "Now I can replace my foolish pride with a gift of love for Jesus. Willingly, I will share his destiny."

So the Aspen became the wood of the cross. To this day, Aspen trees still have trembling, shivering leaves, a reminder of their gift of love, which is the true meaning of Christmas. It is said that along with all the other trees, Aspens bow toward Bethlehem each Christmas Eve, honoring the Christ Child who gave his life that others may live.

♦ ♦ ♦ ♦

There are many traditions and stories associated with the holly, or ilex, tree that connect it with both Christmas and Easter. Sometimes it is called the "Holy Tree," since one story maintains that it first grew in Christ's footsteps. Another story asserts that holly was the tree of the cross, and the crown of thorns was made from its spiky, jagged leaves. In Germany, holly is called Christdorn, in memory of the crown of thorns placed on Christ's head by the mocking soldiers.

One story of the holly tree tells of a time when all the trees in the forest refused to allow their wood to be used for the cross.

The Holly Tree and the Cross

A woodcutter was sent into the forest to get wood for Jesus' cross. But each tree the woodcutter chose, rather than be part of the Crucifixion, splintered into tiny fragments at the touch of the ax.

"Not me," said Maple.

"Not me," said Oak.

"Not me," said Spruce and Cedar and Pine.

Then came Holly's turn. As the woodcutter swung his ax, Holly remembered how the Christ Child had smiled when she had been woven into a crown for the little King. Holly recalled the baby's touch, turning her leaves green and her berries red.

"Well," she thought, "I will not refuse Jesus now. The Holy Infant has become the Man of Sorrows, and I will go with him."

Holly submitted to the ax and was formed into a cross. She allowed her branches to be made into the crown of thorns so as to suffer the shame of Crucifixion with the Savior of the world. Holly was sad that the Christmas crown woven from her branches would now become the Easter crown of thorns, but she loved her Savior and knew that it was the right thing to do.

Mistletoe

In the days when Jesus walked the earth, Mistletoe was a great and powerful tree, stronger than any other tree in the forest. For that reason his branches were selected to make the wood of the cross.

At first he considered this to be an honor and was quite

pleased with himself. But after watching the Crucifixion, Mistletoe realized he had been used for a dreadful purpose. He felt so bad about it that he determined never again to be a tall, proud tree. Instead, he would be a trailing plant that grew from other trees, relying on them for his life. As further atonement, Mistletoe vowed to bestow gifts of peace and blessing upon anyone who walked beneath him, thus becoming a mirror reflecting the love of Christ.

♦ ♦ ♦ ♦

In French, mistletoe is known as *Herbe de la Croix*, or "herb of the cross," while in Latin it is called *Lignum Sanctae Crucis*, or "wood of the sacred cross." In time, mistletoe became a symbol of divine love and healing, which it remains today. Our popular tradition of kissing under the mistletoe derived from this story. Just as mistletoe relies on other trees for survival, we too must rely on the Holy Infant of Bethlehem for our Christian existence. In that way we, like mistletoe, will become a reflection of Christ's love.

Family and Group Activities

1. Discuss feelings of sadness, anger, resentment, and other negative attitudes that one might feel during the

Christmas season. Just as the little donkey with a tear in his eye felt great sadness about Jesus, we need to acknowledge and understand our emotions and realize that it is all right to be sad sometimes. Write down negative thoughts and tear the paper into bits to symbolize that you have power over depressing ideas. Ask Jesus to help you in forgiving yourself and others for doing and saying hurtful things. Repeat this gesture as often as necessary, while recalling that Jesus told us that we are to forgive again and again.

2. As in the story of mistletoe, share God's love with others. Hang a branch of mistletoe over your front door and welcome all who enter with a hug or kiss.

3. End a Christmas dinner or other holiday gathering with an activity called "Creative Giving." Write the name of each person on a separate sheet of paper, and distribute the sheets with pencils. Everyone gives a compliment to the person named on the paper and passes it along. Each participant adds something agreeable or attractive that they admire about that person. Send the paper along until each individual has added an appreciative comment about every other person in the group. Designate someone to read the comments, and then watch the surprised, delighted faces of the recipients as the sheets are read.

Craft Suggestions

1. Make bookmarks. Find pictures in old magazines or Christmas cards, then cut, laminate, and glue the pictures to large paperclips, adding glitter if it's available. Colorful vinyl-coated paperclips work nicely for this activity. Paperclip bookmarks make a useful token to give as a favor, enclose in a letter, or present with a gift book.

2. For the littlest ones in your family or group, draw an outline of a Christmas tree using a green crayon on white paper. Ask the children to decorate the tree with their own artwork, stickers, or pictures cut from magazines and Christmas cards. Send the tree as a unique card to a family member or special friend.

Christmas Bells

Among the oldest traditions of Christmas is the ringing of bells. According to an early story, throughout the world on Christmas Eve, bells ring joyously to announce the birth of the Infant King. Even bells that have been buried through earthquakes or lost at sea continue this ritual. It is said that if you put your ear to the earth on Christmas Eve, you can still hear the joyful peal of bells welcoming the Christ Child.

Another early story declares that on that first Christmas Eve, all the bells in the world began tolling an hour before midnight. Their solemn tone was to warn the forces of darkness that the Light of the World was about to be born. At the stroke of midnight, the funereal tenor of the bells changed to a joyous pealing, a wondrous musical chime announcing the birth of the newborn King.

Based on this account, medieval churches developed a tradition of somberly tolling the bells an hour before midnight on Christmas Eve. This practice spread throughout Europe, becoming known in England as "tolling the devil's knell." The tradition of declaring that Christ's birth announced the devil's death is still observed today in Yorkshire, where ringing of the Christmas Eve bell has continued for more than seven hundred years. The bell is tolled one time for every year since the birth of Christ, to let everyone know that the devil has been defeated. As in the story, the last stroke is timed to toll exactly at midnight, when the tone of the bell changes to one of triumph and joy.

Bells, suspended as they are in soaring church towers, form a link between heaven and earth, summoning the faithful to communion with the Divine. Known as the voice of the church, chiming bells are God's messengers that call us to worship and prayer. Their intensity and compelling force penetrate deeply into the human heart. With their pitch and rhythms indicating joy or sorrow, church bells ringing throughout the year are a lovely symbol of the heavenly.

In the days just before Easter, however, most Christian churches silence their bells as a way to remember the death of Jesus. The bells stop after church services on Maundy Thursday and remain still throughout Good Friday and Holy Saturday. Then, at midnight on Holy Saturday, the bells ring once again, announcing the risen Christ. This tradition is continued in many European churches today. Some of the churches maintain the tradition of ringing the bells all night, but the more common practice is to begin the joyful pealing of bells at the Easter sunrise service.

According to one charming account, at the sound of bells on Easter morning the sun begins dancing in honor of Christ's return to life. Particularly well known in Europe, the story describes how the dancing sun accompanies rays of light that are the same Christmas angels who announced the birth of Jesus, now dancing for joy over his rebirth.

The renewal of light at the hour of sunrise is a lovely symbol of Christ's return to life. The sound of the bells symbolizes to some the Word of God at the moment of creation, and to others the music of the spheres, which John Milton wrote became audible at the birth of Christ. Everything that has come into being—every star, planet, creature, person, blade of grass—is part of the process in which light is brought out of darkness through the creative word of God that is eternally present at all times and in all places. As written in the Bible:

> In the beginning was the Word, and the Word was with God, and the Word was God.... Through him all things were made; without him nothing was made that has been made. In him was life, and that life was the light of men. (John 1:1-4)

This Light of Life, reflected in the music of the spheres, is believed to be so ideal in its beauty and purity that it is nothing less than the perfect harmony achieved by God at the moment of creation. The bells of Christmas, echoing the divine music, still call us to worship the Baby of Bethlehem.

♦ ♦ ♦ ♦

When the Christ Child came into this world, he brought with him the deep meaning of life, which is love. As the stories of Christmas show, everything in the universe speaks to us of God's love. We do not have to be in sacred places to see God's work all around us; the stars in the sky, the flowers on the hillside, the animals in the forest, and the people we meet all speak to us of God.

Once we invite Jesus into our heart, we participate with all creation in embracing and honoring the Savior. The message of Christmas is that we are not alone. As Jesus promised, he is with us always, sharing our joys and sorrows, and nothing can ever separate us from his love. Perhaps as we read the Christmas stories, we will begin to understand more fully the joy of Christmas and the hope of Easter, which are summed up in the triumphant words of Jesus:

Do not let your hearts be troubled....
Because I live, you also will live. (John 14:1, 19)